S.P.I.R.E.®

Specialized Program Individualizing Reading Excellence

3rd Edition

Workbook
Level 1

Sheila Clark-Edmands

School Specialty, Inc.
Cambridge and Toronto

Editorial Project Manager: Tracey Newman
Senior Editor: Laura A. Woollett
Assistant Editor: Rachel L. Smith

Printed in Benton Harbor, MI, in July 2011
ISBN 978-0-8388-5701-4

1 2 3 4 5 PPG 15 14 13 12 11

sad	nap	ask	lab	ham
and	mad	ram	pan	jam

_____

- - - - - - - - - - - -

_____

_____

- - - - - - - - - - - -

_____

_____

- - - - - - - - - - - -

Pam's Bag

_____

Pam has a _____ .

The bag is _____ .

_____

The bag has a _____ .

_____

The bag has _____ .

rags   tag   bag   fat

Hal had a nap.

Al and the cat sat.

Jan ran fast.

Jan is at the lab.

Tad swam a lap.

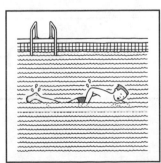

At Bat

_____

- -

Jan has a _____ .

_____

- -

The pal is _____ .

_____

- -

Hal has a _____ .

_____

- -

Jan has a _____ .

Hal   cap   bat   pal

glad   cat   tag   fan   bat

plant   rag   nap   hat   jam

The Ant

_____

- - - - - - - - - - - - - - -

Jan has an _____ .

_____

- - - - - - - - - - - - - - -

The ant is _____ .

_____

- - - - - - - - - - - - - - -

The ant is _____ .

_____

- - - - - - - - - - - - - - -

Jan has a _____ .

_____

- - - - - - - - - - - - - - -

The cat has the _____ .

_____

- - - - - - - - - - - - - - -

The cat is _____ .

_____

| ant | cat | fat |
| ant | sad | tan |

_____

Pam can tag Sal.

Tad has a ram.

Pam has a tag.

Jan is glad.

Nan is mad.

Jan has a hat and a bag.

The Cat

Sam has a _____.

The cat _____.

Sam can _____ the cat.

Sam _____ the cat.

The cat is _____.

The cat ran at _____.

Sam ran and _____.

pat   ran   tags   mad   sat   Sam   cat

hat	zap	cap	ham
cap	lab	Sam	cab
cab	mat	nab	sap

pat	rat	bag	sag
bag	pan	van	tax
man	tag	ax	ran

flag	tap	jam	mat
flap	jab	plan	Dan
crab	bag	hat	ram

Al's Pal

Al has a _____.

The pal is _____.

Al and Dan _____.

Al and Dan had a _____.

Dan   ran   pal   nap

sit   sip   grin   flip   pit

mix   dig   hit   swim   tip

The Bad Van

The man is in the _____.

The man is _____.

His van did _____.

The van has a _____.

The man _____ fix it.

can   flat   mad   van   sit

The kid will tip it.

The kid will hit it.

Jan is fast.

Jan is last.

Bill had a bit.

Bill had a bat.

Jan is sad.

Jan is glad.

Tim will pass it.

Tim will hit it.

Bill can dig.

Bill has a bag.

13

Sad Jim

_____

- -

Jim is _____.

_____

- -

Jim bit his _____.

_____

- -

Jim hit his _____.

_____

- -

Jim did rip his _____.

cap   lip   hip   sad

traffic   win   jig   sip   flip

clam   pig   hit   dip   rabbit

The Pig and the Ant

_____

The pig hid in the _____.

The pig had a _____.

An ant bit the _____.

The pig _____.

The ant had a _____.

nap   pit   ran   pig   nap

Dad did kiss Dan.

Pam had a hit.

The pig hid.

The pig had a nap.

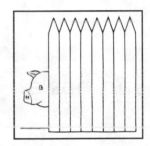

Jan has a big gift.

The cat has a bib.

Jan's Rag Bag

Jan has a _____.

The bag has a _____.

The rip is _____.

Jan has a _____.

Jan can _____ the rip.

_____

big   rip   bag   fix   pin

_____

Jan did win.

The cat is in a can.

The pig is fat.

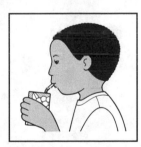

Tim bit it.

The cat had a nap.

Jim will sip it.

A Bad Hit

Dan has a tin _____.

The tin can hits the _____.

The man in the van is _____.

Dan is in a _____.

Dad can fix the _____.

jam   van   can   mad   van

dog   stop   hot   top   rod
log   drop   hop   frog   pot

The Hot Hot Dog

_____

Sam got a _____ .

Sam _____ the hot dog.

The hot dog is _____ !

Sam has a hot _____ .

Sam got a can and had a _____ .

hot dog   hot   bit   sip   lip

fox   log   hit   frog   clam
hot   cat   stop   drop   rod

The Hot Rod

_____

Bob and Tom sat in the _____ .

The hot rod is in the _____ .

The hot rod sat and _____ .

The hot rod had a bad _____ .

Bob and Tom did not _____ .

win   sat   rod   pit   hot rod

The dog is in the bag.

Dad can spin the pot.

The dog is in the box.

The tot is mad.

The dog has a basket.

Sam is hot.

Sam and the Fox

_____

The fox sat in a big _____.

Sam had a _____.

Sam got hot and _____

on the _____.

The fox did _____ at Sam.

_____

| grin | sat | log | jog | log |

_____

It is not on.

The grill is hot.

Sam bit a hot dog.

Tim is on top of Dad.

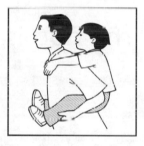

Dan and Tom had a jog.

The tot did drop it.

The Lost Dog

Bob _____ his dog.

The dog _____ in a box.

The box is in the _____.

The dog is _____.

The dog got _____ the van.

Bob is _____.

van	lost	sad
off	glad	hid

I can hit it.
I am glad I had a rag.

It is in the van.
I can fix it!

Pig, Hog, Fox, Dog

A pig is a _____.

A fox is _____ a dog.

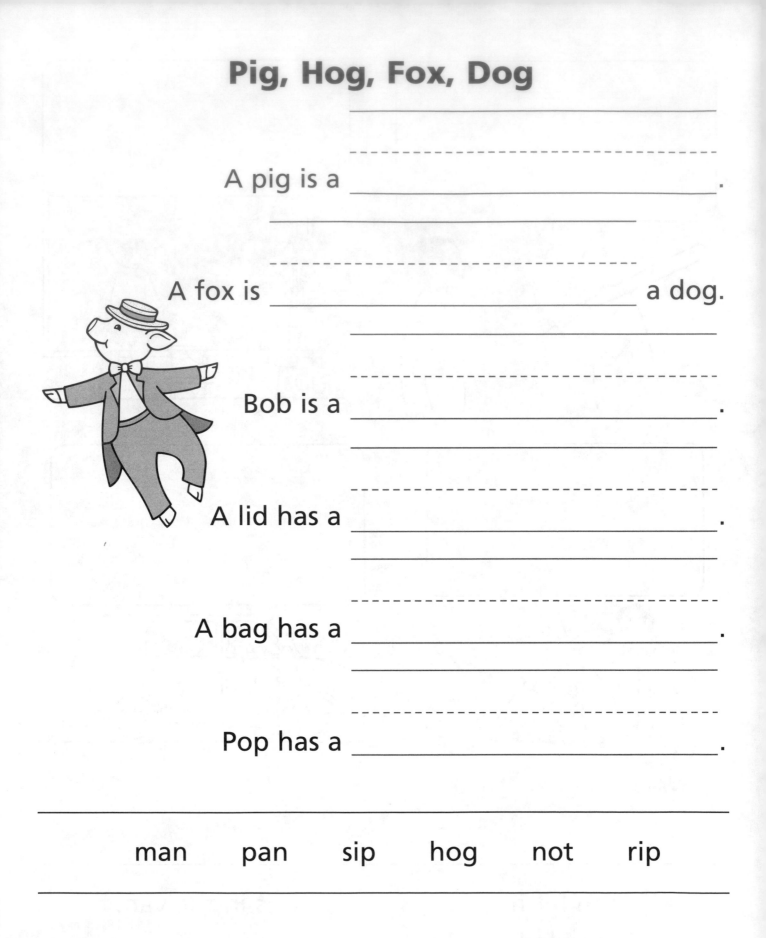

Bob is a _____.

A lid has a _____.

A bag has a _____.

Pop has a _____.

man   pan   sip   hog   not   rip

drum   bus   run   mud   up

cut   mug   jump   nut   tub

The Gum

_____

Sam had fun in the _____.

_____

Sam got _____.

_____

Sam sat on a _____.

_____

The log had _____ on it.

_____

The gum got on Sam's _____.

_____

Dad got the gum _____.

_____

Sam is _____.

gum   off   pants   sun   log   glad   hot

scrub   cup   muffin   mug   bug
nut   rug   gift   hug   suds

_____   _____   _____

- - - - - - - - -   - - - - - - - - -   - - - - - - - - -

_____   _____   _____

- - - - - - - - -   - - - - - - - - -   - - - - - - - - -

_____   _____   _____

- - - - - - - - -   - - - - - - - - -   - - - - - - - - -

_____   _____   _____

Mud, Mud

The dog _____ in the mud.

Tim _____ in the mud.

The _____ is hot.

The mud is _____ hot.

Tim _____ in the mud.

Tim got in the _____.

The mud is _____ Tim.

Mom is _____!

tub   sun   ran   sat   dug   not   glad   off

Bill is up on top.

Jan's hand is up.

The tot dug in the sand.

The pup is in the tub.

Jim hit the drum.

The sun is up.

The Hot Sip

Tim has a _____.

The cup is _____.

Tim has a _____.

The cup did tip on Tim's _____.

Tim got a _____.

Tim did _____ his hand and his lip.

hand   tip   hot   cup   rub   rag   sip

It can blast off.

The kids got on the bus.

Jan and Bob run.

The top is not up.

The pup is not hot.

Tim is up on top.

The Cab

_____

Dan has a _____ .

The cab had a _____ .

The hubcap is in the _____ .

Dan's pal Sam got a _____ .

Sam did _____ the hubcap.

The cab can _____ .

| hubcap | mud | cab |
| run | rub | rag |

An Ant in a Bun

_____

- -

Sam has a _____ .

_____

- -

The hot dog is in a _____ .

_____

- -

An _____ got in the bun.

_____

- -

Sam _____ the hot dog and bun.

_____

- -

The ant _____ on Sam.

_____

- -

An ant in a bun is not _____ .

_____

| sun | ran | bit | ant | bun | hot dog | fun |

cliff   jet   net   help   eggs
wet   sled   hem   tent   basket

Ben, the Dog

Ben is at the _____.

The _____ is hot.

Ben can dig up a _____.

Ben can dig a big _____.

Ben has a _____ in the pond.

Ben is _____, but Ben is _____ hot.

not   bug   dip   sun   pond   wet   pit

bonnet   skillet   men   basket   cliff
rabbit   sled   helmet   cactus   hot dog

_____

- - - - - - - - - - -

_____

- - - - - - - - - - -

_____

- - - - - - - - - - -

Rex, the Tin Man

_____

Rex is a _____.

Rex has a tin _____.

Rex has a tin _____.

Rex is in a _____.

The van is lost in a _____.

Rex can _____.

Rex went in the _____.

box   rust   tent   wet fog   hat   tin man   leg

Fred got a pet.

Fred got wet.

Ted will hug his dad.

Ted will help his dad.

Mom will hem it.

Mom will hum it.

Tom fed his pet.

Tom hid his pet.

Meg and Dan did trip on the step.

Meg and Dan went on a trip.

The tot will hit the leg.

The tot will hit the peg.

44

The Red Ant

Jan sat on a _____.

The log had a red _____ on it.

A red ant _____ Jan on the _____.

Jan got the ant in a _____.

Jan met _____.

The ant is in Tim's _____.

Jan is _____ Tim has the ant.

| net | glad | ant | log | leg | bit | box | Tim |

Jill has a big basket.

Dan can lift it!

Nan did not hit the net.

Mom will hem the dress.

The dog is at the vet.

Ted will help Dad.

The Pet Hen

_____

Deb had a pet _____ hen.

The hen _____ in the pen.

The hen did not let _____ in.

The hen did not get _____ .

The hen did _____ and _____ .

The hen had an _____ !

Deb had a _____ .

sat	egg	Deb	red
hop	grin	hop	fed

47

The man will help Ted swim.

Ted will help his dad.

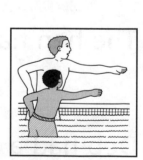

Tim has a trim.

The jet is fast.

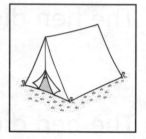

Dad and the kids will camp in a tent.

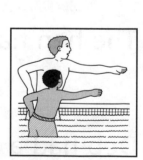

Tom fed his pet.

A Gift from a Pal

_____

- -

Fred sat on the top _____.

_____

- -

Fred felt _____.

_____

- -

His best pal Sam had a pet _____, and

_____

- -

Fred did _____.

_____

- -

Fred gets a _____ from Sam.

_____

- -

It is a pet frog in a _____.

_____   _____

- - - - - - - - - - - - - -   - - - - - - - - - - - - - -

The pet frog can _____ and _____.

_____

not   gift   frog   glum   jump   step   box   hop

_____

ten   bed   golf   web   basket

desk   peg   dentist   tennis   best

rod   dig   wet   puppet   hot dog

jump   nip   run   nap   button

basket   win   clam   hit   hot
hem   peg   tent   gift   pig

_____

___ ___ ___ ___ ___ ___ ___

_____

- - - - - - - - - - - - - - -

_____

- - - - - - - - - - - - - - -

_____

- - - - - - - - - - - - - - -

_____

_____

lash   crib   shop   fish   ship
brush   shut   wish   bonnet   hush

Sad Fred

Fred had fish and hash on his _____ .

Fred _____ his lip.

It was a _____ .

Then Fred hit his _____ on the tub.

Fred was a _____ .

Fred's cat had the _____ .

Fred's dog had the _____ .

dish   hash   bit   fish   cut   pad   shin   mess

a mess you had.

mash   shop   smash   ship   lash
cash   fish   sash   wish   brush

It did smash.

Tom can brush.

Pam can wish.

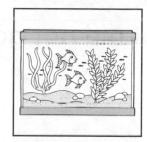

Nan can mash it.

The man has lots of cash.

Dan has fish.

The Fish Wish

I had a _____

I had a _____ .

I had a big _____ on the rod.

I did not get the fish _____ the rod.

I got help from _____ .

The fish did a _____ in the net.

The fish got us _____ .

The fish got its _____ .

| net | wish | fish | flip | wet | rod | Tim | off |

a sad fish in a net.

The Ant in the Box

An ant was _____ in a box.

The box had a _____ .

The cat did _____ the box.

Then the _____ got the box.

The dog did _____ the lid off.

The ant ran _____ .

The ant hid in the _____ rug.

The cat and dog _____ get the ant.

mash   lid   dog   shut   did not   shag   fast   rip

 **a big ant.**

Is It in Mom's Bags?

fish	can	nuts	men	dad
dust	bed	pop	chat	ham
gum	buns	ox	mop	milk
dog	rat	box	hat	fast
cash	trash	ship	frog	dish
pig	pen	jam	web	bench
eggs	hash			

catch   sandwich   chop   chat   chess
punch   cash   chin   trash   bunch

The Pigpen

_____

The pig sat on the _____ .

Sam got the pig _____ .

The pig ran off in a _____ .

Sam did _____ in the mud.

Sam sat in the _____ .

Sam had mud on his _____ .

Sam got a _____ from the pig.

kiss   rush   off   pigpen   chin   mud   slip   bench

a big kiss on the chin.

chill   list   gift   bench   ship

win   chin   brush   kiss   munch

a i o u e

d _____ sh

d _____ sh

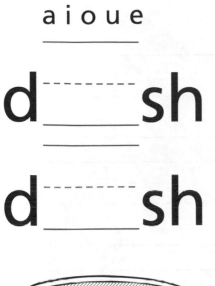

a i o u e

sh _____ p

sh _____ p

a i o u e

b _____ nch

b _____ nch

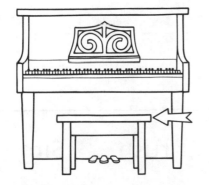

a i o u e

l _____ nch

At Lunch

_____

Miss Sim's class had _____.

Ben and Chad sat on the _____.

Ben and Chad did _____.

Ben and Chad did not get

_____

_____.

Miss _____

did ask Sam to get Ben and Chad.

_____

Ben and Chad did _____ to

Miss Sim's class.

_____

up   bench   lunch   chat   rush   Sim

the best lunch I had.

ship   shop   chess   chop   chin   lash
wish   bench   dash   fish   lunch   chat

ch   sh

Tim has sand at lunch.
Tim has a hot dog and milk.
Tim has a sandwich at lunch.

Chad can catch it.
Dad cannot catch it.
Dad can catch it.

Sam sat on gum.
Sam sat on a big dog.
Sam can chop the log.

Ron can punch it.
Ron can sip the punch.
Ron can munch and munch.

Tom has a big log.
Tom did chop ten logs.
Tom can lift the logs.

Jill is a champ.
Jill is a chimp.
Jill did not run fast.

A Nap Is Not Fun

The tot did not _____.

Mom got the tot in _____.

The tot got _____.

A nap is not _____ fun.

The tot hit his _____ on the bed.

The tot did _____!

The tot sat in Mom's _____.

Mom cannot _____ until the tot naps.

much   chin   rest   mad   hush   lap   yell   bed

jet   moth   cloth   bath   thin
fish   that   clip   path   math

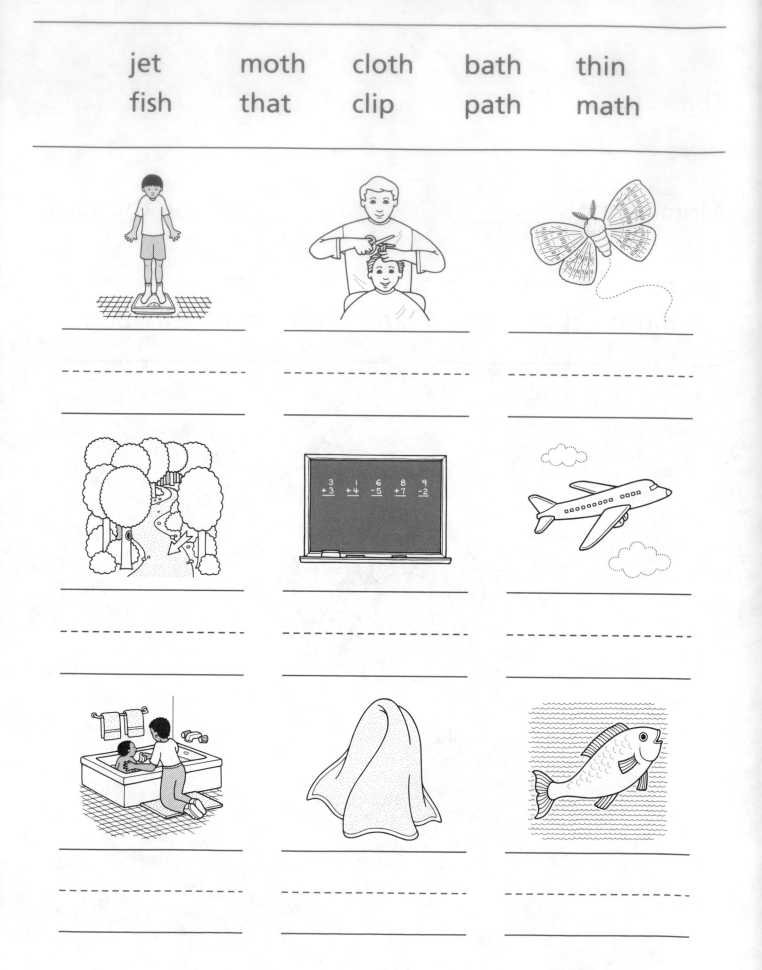

The Bug

_____

- - - - - - - - - - - - - - - - - -

Chad and Chip ran _____.

_____

- - - - - - - - - - - - - - - - - -

A bug sat _____.

_____

- - - - - - - - - - - - - - - - - -

Then the bug sat _____.

_____

- - - - - - - - - - - - - - - - - -

Then the bug sat _____.

_____

- - - - - - - - - - - - - - - - - -

Chad and Chip _____.

_____

- - - - - - - - - - - - - - - - - -

The bug sat _____.

_____

on a log	did dash
on the path	on Chad's lip
on Chip's chin	on Chip's leg

_____

vest

(st)

best	test	mast	must
last	nest	fist	bust
rest	west	mist	trust

Sam had the _____ lunch.

A robin was in the _____.

Tom ran _____ Jim and won.

That bug is a _____.

Tim had a _____ in bed.

nest   pest   rest   best   past

A Bug in the Shed

Sam sat _____.

Sam had his dog, Thud, _____.

The bug _____.

The bug _____.

The bug _____.

The bug _____!

---

sat on Sam's leg	in his shed
with him	went buzz, buzz, buzz
bit Thud on the chin	was a pest

Ted is with his mom and dad.

The tot has a nap with
his mom and dad.

Sam has a nap with his dog.

The tot has a nap with his mom.

Pam is with Mom and Dad.

The tot has a bath.

1. The men chat.

2. Jill is ill.

3. What a flash!

4. Mom felt Jill, and Jill is hot.

5. Tom, Tim, and Dan chat.

6. The man is rich.

7. The man will rest at his desk.

8. The trash fell from the basket.

9. The man had cash.

10. The man slept.

11. The flash is big.

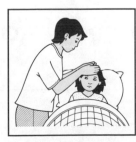

12. The trash is a big mess.

hum	chop
shop	gum
ship	chip

fan	cat
pig	big
that	man

last	end
and	fast
bend	hand

went	bed
red	trip
slip	tent

than	can
whip	then
when	chip

tax	ten
wish	fish
when	wax

Dash on the Path

_____

The kids did dash _____.

The dog ran _____.

The dog _____.

The kids and the dog sat _____.

The kids let the dog _____.

Then the kids and the dog _____.

did nap   munch on the lunch

on a bench   with them

was fast   on the path

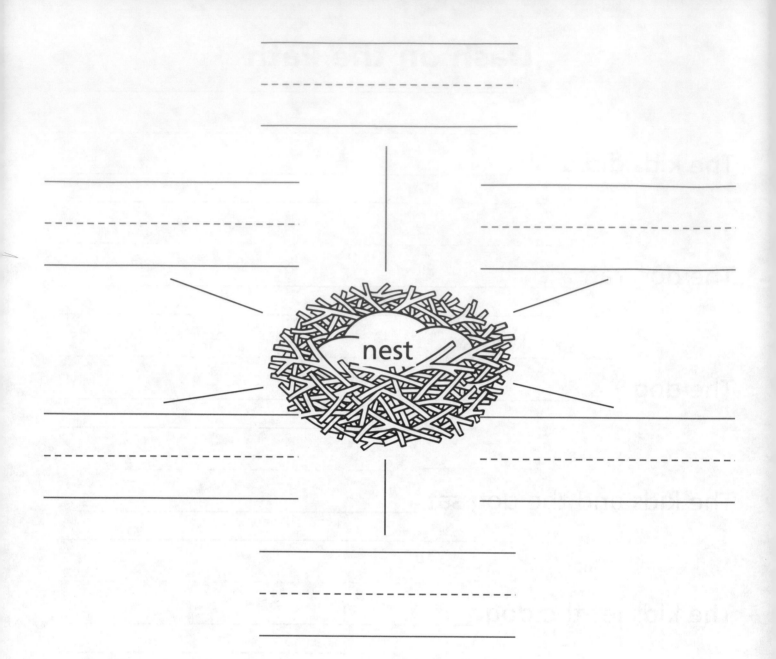

twigs   eggs   dogs   grass

string   bugs   robin   fish

The Lost Dog

_____

Sam ran with his _____.

Sam and Spot ran ten _____.

Sam sat on a _____ to rest.

Spot had a rest with _____.

Then Spot ran up a _____.

When Spot was lost, Sam felt _____.

dog   sad   him   bench   laps   path

then

Then tells us what will happen next.
Tom will mix it. Then Tom will flip it.

_____

- -

1. Tom will _____ .

_____

- -

2. Tom will _____ .

Ted will run fast. Then Ted will rest.
Ted will run. What will happen next?

_____

- -

Ted will _____ .

The bus will stop. Then it will get gas.
The bus will stop. What will happen next?

_____

- -

The bus will _____ .

when

When tells us when a thing will happen.

When Tom gets a job, Tom will get cash.
When will Tom get cash?

_____

- -

_____

The cat will rest when it gets in the bed.
When will the cat rest?

_____

- -

_____

The cup did drop when Al had a sip.
When did the cup drop?

_____

- -

_____

The cat had lunch when Bob fed it.
When did the cat get lunch?

_____

- -

_____

Ant Facts

An ant is an _____.

An ant has six _____.

An ant can _____.

Ants can dig in the _____.

An ant has lots of _____.

An ant has a big _____.

legs   dig   sand   insect   eggs   nest

A Whiz Kid

Jen is a _____ .

Jen can _____ .

When is Jen a whiz? _____

When is Jen not a whiz? _____

whiz kid	add fast	at lunch
at math	when Jen spells	with a top

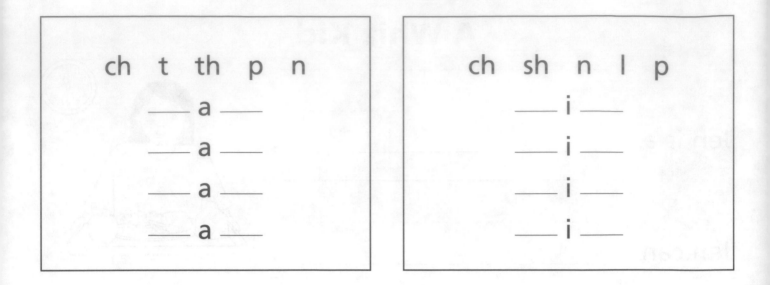

ch t th p n

___ a ___

___ a ___

___ a ___

___ a ___

ch sh n l p

___ i ___

___ i ___

___ i ___

___ i ___

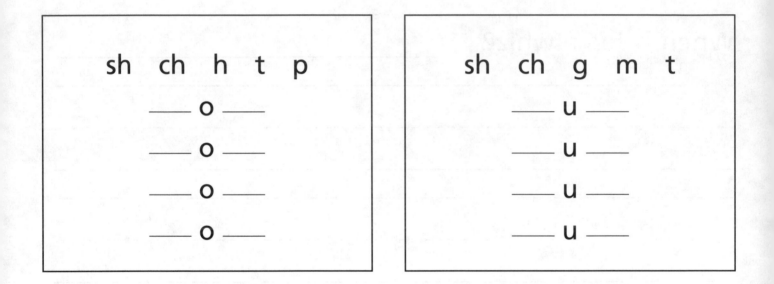

sh ch h t p

___ o ___

___ o ___

___ o ___

___ o ___

sh ch g m t

___ u ___

___ u ___

___ u ___

___ u ___

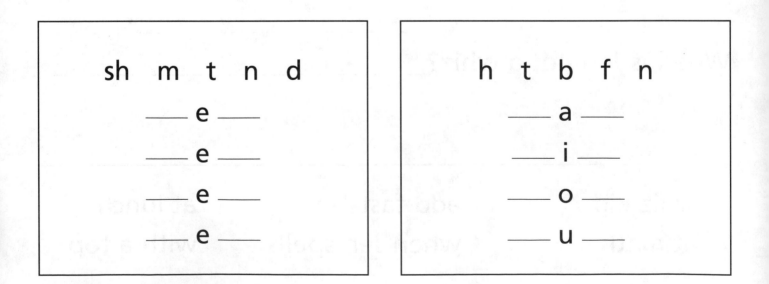

sh m t n d

___ e ___

___ e ___

___ e ___

___ e ___

h t b f n

___ a ___

___ i ___

___ o ___

___ u ___

Chip's Job

What did Chip want to get? _____

What was Chip's problem? _____

What job did Chip get? _____

 Chip at his job with his pet.

tent	dent	bent	spent
runt	grunt	lent	pants
slant	rent	stunt	ant
plant	went	blunt	grant

nd

and	mend	end	brand
grand	spend	bend	sand
stand	band	send	fond
pond	land	lend	tend

The bug stung Jan <u>when</u> Jan sat on it.

The king lost his ring <u>when</u> the king was on the swing.

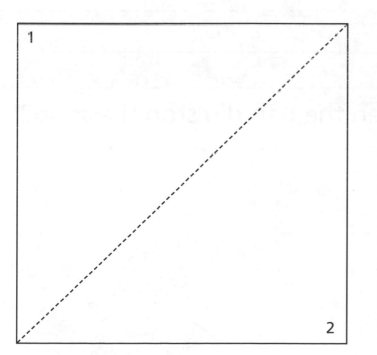

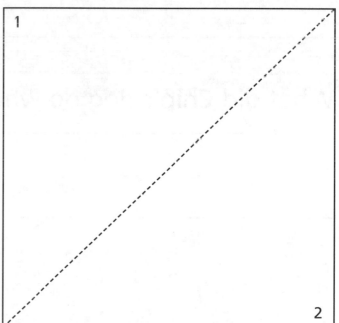

Beth will sit.
<u>Then</u> Beth will run.

Chad will drop the brush.
<u>Then</u> the dog will bring it.

Stop the Song

Who sang with Jim?

_____

- -

_____

What did the pals sing?

_____

- -

_____

What did Jim's mom want them to do?

_____

- -

_____

What did Chip's dog do when the pals did stop the song?

_____

- -

_____

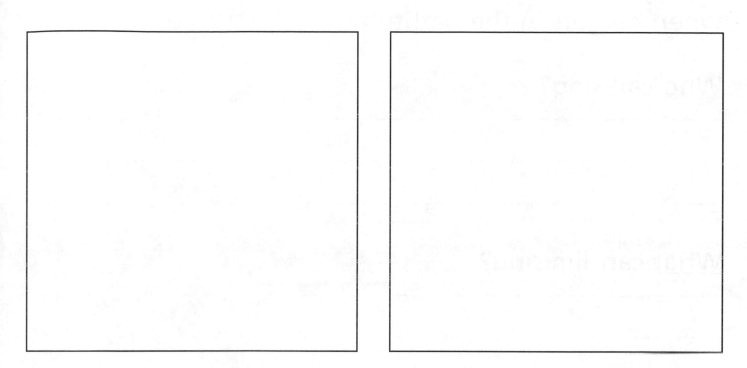

The king will not swing.

Tim's hand is in a sling.

The bug stung Tom.

Mom hangs up the hat.

Jim can sing a song. His song is long.
Jim can sing a rap. Jim will sing the rap
when he gets in the bathtub.

<u>Who</u> can sing?

_____

- -

_____

<u>What</u> can Jim sing?

_____

- -

_____

<u>When</u> will Jim sing?

_____

- -

_____

Sam had a pet frog. When Sam
left the lid off the box,
the frog went to the pond.
Sam sat on a log and felt sad.

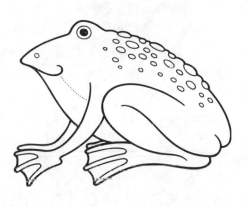

<u>Who</u> had a pet frog?

_____

_ _

_____

<u>When</u> did the frog hop to the pond?

_____

_ _

_____

<u>What</u> did Sam do?

_____

_ _

_____

The Vet

Fred's cat had to get a _____.

The cat went with Dad and Fred to the _____.

The vet had a _____.

The big tan dog did _____.

The cat did jump and _____.

Fred had to get his cat _____,
and the cat got his shot.

run into the van	shot	next
yelp at the cat	vet	long list
from the van		

The Lost Ring

What was the man?

_____

\- -

The man was _____ .

What was lost?

_____

\- -

The _____ was lost.

When was it lost?

_____

\- -

It was lost when _____ .

Who is the king's pet?

_____

\- -

The king's pet is _____ .

What did happen when Fang dug in the grass?

What will the king do with his ring when next he swings?

-ng	-nk

rink   thank   clang   sank   sunk   sung   swing   sang
stink   stung   think   ring   thing   drink   bring

A Bug Sting

What was on the bench? _____

What did happen when Jan sat on the bench?

_____

- -

_____

_____

- -

What did Jan's mom do? _____

The bug had big wings. _____

Jan's hand was pink from the sting. _____

Jan said, "That was a bad sting!" _____

Mom said, "Bugs sing." _____

100

Tom's Desk

What did happen when Tom got a pen off his desk?

_____

- -

_____

What did Tom and his pal Sam do to fix Tom's desk?

_____

- -

_____

What can Sam do to fix his desk?

_____

- -

_____

 your desk.

```
┌─────────────────────────────────────────────┐
│                                             │
│                                             │
│                                             │
│                                             │
│                                             │
└─────────────────────────────────────────────┘
```

A Junk Bed

What is a bunk bed? _____

_____

_____

_____

Who has the bottom bunk bed? _____

_____

What did Val do to Nan? _____

_____

_____

What do you think Nan will do? _____

_____

_____

What do you think Nan will tell Val? _____

_____

- - - - - - - - - - - - - - - - - - - -

_____

- - - - - - - - - - - - - - - - - - - -

_____

 your bed.

Hank's Fish Tank

Hank had a big fish tank.

The fish tank had a lid on top.

Hank had ten fish in the tank.

Hank said, "Run, fish, run."

A pink and a red fish swam fast.

The pink fish did not jump.

The pink fish did splash Hank.

Hank thinks the splash is fun.

The Ink Spot

_____

- -

What was in Tim's pen? _____

 What was Tim's problem?

What did Mom think of Tim's problem?

_____

- -

_____

_____

- -

_____

What did Tim do to fix the problem?

_____

- -

_____

_____

- -

_____

A Mink Hat Is Not a Bed

What was Lin's problem?

What was the cat's wish?

Was Lin upset with the cat?

What if a dog was in the hat?

Hank's Wish

What is stinking in Hank's van?

_____

- -

_____

What can Hank do with the stink?

_____

- -

_____

　　　　　　　　　　　　　　　　　　　　　_____

　　　　　　　　　　　　　　　　　　　- - - - - - - - - - - -

Can Hank get the van to the dump? _____

When gas is not in the tank of a van, what happens?

_____

- -

_____

What is Hank's wish?

_____

- -

_____

_____

- -

Who helps Hank get gas? _____